BY SUPPER POSSESSED
Charles M. Schulz

RAVETTE BOOKS

This edition first published by Ravette Books Limited 1989

Printed and bound for Ravette Books Limited,
3 Glenside Estate, Star Road,
Partridge Green, Horsham,
West Sussex RH13 8RA
by The Guernsey Press Company Limited,
Guernsey, Channel Islands.

ISBN 1 85304 127 0

DO YOU THINK YOU'RE A DIFFERENT PERSON FROM WHAT YOU WERE LAST YEAR?

DO YOU THINK YOU'VE REALLY CHANGED?

© 1985 United Feature Syndicate, Inc.

I REMEMBER LAST YEAR YOU SAID YOU WERE GOING TO TRY TO BE A BETTER LISTENER..

WHAT?

1-1-86

THE MEETING OF THE TOBOGGAN CLUB WILL COME TO ORDER..

AS YOU KNOW, TONIGHT IS OUR TOBOGGAN PARTY... WE NEED A VOLUNTEER TO BRING A TUNA CASSEROLE..

1-2-86

GOOD.. WE'LL SEE YOU ALL TONIGHT

© 1985 United Feature Syndicate, Inc.

VERY FEW THINGS IN LIFE MAKE YOU FEEL MORE FOOLISH THAN SITTING ALONE ON A TOBOGGAN IN THE DESERT HOLDING A TUNA CASSEROLE!

Dear

I miss you more each day. I love you more than words can say.

1-3-86

THAT'S NICE, BUT WHO ARE YOU WRITING TO?

I CAN ALWAYS FILL THAT IN LATER..

OH, NO!

1-4-86

I HATE IT WHEN..

..A TUMBLEWEED GETS IN YOUR SLEEPING BAG!

 MY GRANDMOTHER SAYS HER FIRST DATE WAS AN EVENING AT THE OPERA...

1-8-86

 SHE SAYS SHE'LL ALWAYS REMEMBER HOW HER MOTHER INSISTED THAT SHE WEAR WHITE GLOVES

 HOW ABOUT HER DATE? WHO WAS THE BOY?

 WHO KNOWS? ALL SHE REMEMBERS IS THE WHITE GLOVES!

© 1985 United Feature Syndicate, Inc.

 DIGGING FOR RARE EGYPTIAN COINS CAN BE VERY EXCITING...

 IF YOU FIND THE RIGHT ONES, YOU COULD MAKE A FORTUNE..

1-9-86   © 1985 United Feature Syndicate, Inc.

 ALL IT TAKES IS FAITH AND PATIENCE

 UNLESS, OF COURSE, IT SUDDENLY OCCURS TO YOU THAT YOU'RE IN THE WRONG DESERT..

I WONDER WHAT WOULD HAPPEN IF I ASKED THAT LITTLE RED-HAIRED GIRL IF I COULD SIT NEXT TO HER, AND EAT LUNCH...

MAYBE SHE'D TELL ME TO GET LOST, OR THROW A ROCK AT ME OR HIT ME WITH A STICK...

1-14

OR LAUGH IN MY FACE, OR SCREAM FOR HELP OR KICK ME IN THE STOMACH...

I WONDER IF SHE COULD DO ALL THOSE THINGS AT ONCE..

I'M TIRED OF BEING WISHY-WASHY! I'M GONNA WALK RIGHT OVER, AND TALK TO THAT LITTLE RED-HAIRED GIRL!

I'M DOING IT! I'M COMMITTED! NOTHING CAN STOP ME NOW!

ABSOLUTELY NOTHING!

1-15

WHAT WOULD HAPPEN IF YOU AND I NEVER GOT MARRIED AND LEFT HOME?

WHAT IF YOU AND I HAD TO LIVE TOGETHER FOR THE REST OF OUR LIVES?

1-16 © 1986 United Feature Syndicate, Inc.

DON'T SCARE ME LIKE THAT...IT'S TOO HARD ON MY HAIR!

1-17
A FINE DOG YOU ARE! I'LL BET YOU DON'T EVEN REMEMBER MY NAME!

MY INITIALS ARE C.B., AND MY FIRST NAME IS THE SAME AS THE FAMOUS ACTOR, CHAPLIN...

MY LAST NAME RHYMES WITH 'CROWN'

HINTS! I NEED MORE HINTS!

© 1986 United Feature Syndicate, Inc.

1-19

IT'S FUNNY HOW YOU CAN GO THROUGH LIFE THINKING YOU'VE SEEN EVERYTHING...

THEN, YOU SUDDENLY REALIZE THERE ARE MILLIONS OF THINGS YOU'VE NEVER SEEN BEFORE

NOBODY APPRECIATES HOW WISHY-WASHY PEOPLE SUFFER..

1-18

OUR LIVES ARE IN CONSTANT TORMENT

YOU KNOW WHAT WISHY-WASHY PEOPLE NEED?

© 1986 United Feature Syndicate, Inc.

CRINGE BENEFITS!

SCHULZ

"FUNDING FOR THIS PROGRAM WAS PROVIDED BY DONATIONS FROM OUR VIEWERS..."

1-20   © 1986 United Feature Syndicate, Inc.

"AND WASTED BY A PRODUCER WHO DIDN'T KNOW WHAT HE WAS DOING.."

SCHULZ

YES, MA'AM, I LEFT MY LUNCH BOX ON THE CURB BY THE BUS STOP...

1-23

SOMEONE'S PROBABLY FOUND IT BY NOW

I JUST HOPE WHOEVER FOUND IT APPRECIATES A GOOD LUNCH...

NO DOUGHNUTS !?!

© 1986 United Feature Syndicate, Inc.

THIS IS MY REPORT ON THE "KILLER BEES"

MANY PEOPLE ARE WORRIED ABOUT THE "KILLER BEES"

1-24

© 1986 United Feature Syndicate, Inc.

NOT ME

WHAT I WORRY ABOUT ARE THOSE "KILLER D-MINUSES"!

Dear National Geographic Society, Let's say a person had two-dozen marshmallows.

And let's say he threw all of them at once at a big cactus.

How many do you think would stick?

1-27 © 1986 United Feature Syndicate, Inc.

Are you interested in knowing?

Schulz

THESE CATALOGS WITH THEIR MODELS ARE DEPRESSING! EVERYONE IS HANDSOME AND BEAUTIFUL!

LOOK AT THEM IN THEIR NEW SPRING CLOTHES...IT SETS AN IMPOSSIBLE STANDARD FOR US KIDS...

NONE OF US CAN EVER GROW UP TO LOOK THAT GOOD

1-28

I WILL!

I KNOW I SAW THEIR AD HERE SOMEPLACE..

"PIZZA TO GO".. "PIZZA TO ORDER"..

"PIZZA AT YOUR DOOR"...

1-29

AH, HERE IT IS... "PIZZA FOR RENT"

© 1986 United Feature Syndicate, Inc.

SCHULZ

I DON'T FEEL WELL, BIG BROTHER.. WILL YOU HELP ME WITH MY HOMEWORK?

OF COURSE..IF YOU DON'T FEEL WELL, I'LL BE GLAD TO HELP YOU

WHAT SEEMS TO BE THE TROUBLE?

© 1986 United Feature Syndicate, Inc.

1-30

WHEN I SAW ALL I HAD TO DO, I GOT SICK!

SCHULZ

© 1986 United Feature Syndicate, Inc. 1-31

SOUNDS LIKE A TRAIN GOING THROUGH A TUNNEL, HUH, MA'AM?

 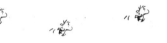 

SO HERE I AM AGAIN RIDING ON THE BACK OF MOM'S BICYCLE...

SHE HAS WHAT IS KNOWN AS A 10-SPEED..

YIPE!

© 1986 United Feature Syndicate, Inc.

ELEVEN, IF YOU COUNT SIDEWAYS!

2-1

ALL THE SNOW IN THIS PART OF THE YARD IS MINE..THE SNOW IN THAT PART OF THE YARD IS YOURS..

1-25 © 1986 United Feature Syndicate, Inc.

I'VE BEEN WONDERING ABOUT SOMETHING...

   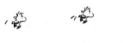

LOOK I MADE THREE DOLLARS SHOVELING SIDEWALKS!

YOU'RE LUCKY WE LIVE WHERE IT SNOWS

YOU'RE RIGHT..I'VE OFTEN WONDERED WHAT IT WOULD BE LIKE TO LIVE WHERE IT DOESN'T SNOW...

SHOVEL YOUR WALK?

2-3
© 1986 United Feature Syndicate, Inc.

Chocolate chip cookies are red.
Chocolate chip cookies are blue.
Chocolate chip cookies are sweet.
So are you.

THIS IS TERRIBLE! I CAN'T MAKE A VALENTINE WITH THAT! WRITE ANOTHER ONE!!

2-9

Angel food cake with seven-minute frosting is red...Angel food cake with seven-minute frosting is blue... Angel food cake with seven-minute frosting is sweet...So are you.

THAT'S THE DUMBEST THING I'VE EVER READ!

I GUESS I MISUNDERSTOOD... I THOUGHT SHE WANTED SOMETHING SENTIMENTAL..

HERE'S THE WORLD WAR I FLYING ACE HIGH OVER NO MAN'S LAND...

2-10

I SUPPOSE YOU THINK YOU'RE FLYING OVER NO MAN'S LAND, HUH?

© 1986 United Feature Syndicate, inc.

WELL, WHAT ABOUT NO WOMAN'S LAND?!

HERE'S THE WORLD WAR I FLYING ACE HIGH OVER NO PERSON'S LAND...

HERE'S THE LONELY WORLD WAR I FLYING ACE SITTING IN A SMALL FRENCH CAFE..

YOUR ROOT BEER, MONSIEUR

I'M IN LOVE! IT'S THE BEGINNING (SIGH) OF ANOTHER TRAGIC ROMANCE...

© 1986 United Feature Syndicate, inc.

2-11

I'VE ONLY BEEN IN FRANCE FOUR HOURS, AND ALREADY I'VE HAD SEVEN TRAGIC ROMANCES!

YOUR NOSE IS WARM, MONSIEUR .. DO YOU FEEL ALL RIGHT?

HAVE YOU HEARD OF THE INFLUENZA EPIDEMIC? THEY SAY SIXTY-FIVE THOUSAND SOLDIERS AT CAMP PONTANEZEN, HERE IN FRANCE, HAVE THE FLU!

2-12

I THINK YOU HAVE A FEVER..

© 1986 United Feature Syndicate, Inc.

IT'S EITHER THE FLU OR LOVE .. THE SYMPTOMS ARE THE SAME...

SCHULZ

HORRORS, MONSIEUR!

2-13

YOU ARE GOING TO FLY EVEN THOUGH YOU ARE ILL WITH INFLUENZA?!

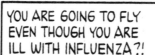

DUTY CALLS! THE WORLD WAR I FLYING ACE MUST CARRY ON!

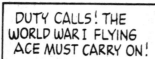

UNLESS I COULD GET A NOTE FROM MY MOTHER..

© 1986 United Feature Syndicate, Inc.

SCHULZ

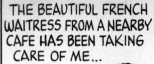

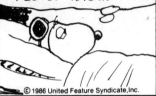

© 1986 United Feature Syndicate, Inc.

2-17

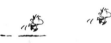 

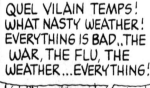

© 1986 United Feature Syndicate, Inc.

2-18

MONSIEUR! GOOD NEWS! GOOD NEWS!

PRESIDENT WILSON SAID THE ARMISTICE WAS SIGNED THIS MORNING!

ARMISTICE

THE WAR IS OVER!!

2-19

WHEN MY GRANDCHILDREN ASK ME WHAT I DID IN THE WAR, I'LL HAVE TO SAY, "I HAD THE FLU!"

SCHULZ

OKAY, I'LL TELL HER

MARCIE WON'T BE IN SCHOOL TODAY, MA'AM.. SHE HAS THE FLU...

SHE SAID SHE GOT IT IN FRANCE WHILE TAKING CARE OF A WORLD WAR I FLYING ACE...

YES, MA'AM... SHE'S WEIRD..

SCHULZ

2-20

LOOK AT THIS LIST OF PEOPLE WHO SUPPORT THE SYMPHONY, SIR...

SEE? THEY HAVE GUARANTORS, BENEFACTORS, SUSTAINERS, SPONSORS, DONORS AND FRIENDS..

2-27

WHERE DO WE FIT IN?

© 1986 United Feature Syndicate, Inc.

WE'RE THE LISTENERS!

I HOPE THIS CONCERT DOESN'T LAST TOO LONG

WHEN DO YOU THINK IT'LL BE OVER?

© 1986 United Feature Syndicate, Inc.

2-28

WHEN THEY PLAY THE LAST NOTE

THANKS, MARCIE!

ARE YOU ENJOYING THE CONCERT, SIR?

SORT OF...THIS IS A LONG PIECE, ISN'T IT?

2-4

YOU HAVE TO CONCENTRATE ON THE MUSIC, AND NOT LET YOUR MIND WANDER..

I THINK MAYBE I'LL HAVE FRENCH TOAST FOR BREAKFAST TOMORROW...

THIS IS MY REPORT ON THE CONCERT WE WENT TO YESTERDAY..

THE MUSIC WAS NICE, AND WE ALL HAD A GOOD TIME..

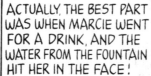 

ACTUALLY, THE BEST PART WAS WHEN MARCIE WENT FOR A DRINK, AND THE WATER FROM THE FOUNTAIN HIT HER IN THE FACE!

2-5

YOU'RE WEIRD, SIR!

© 1986 United Feature Syndicate, Inc.

GOOD AFTERNOON, SIR.. I'M DOING AN ARTICLE FOR OUR SCHOOL PAPER...

HIGH SALARIES AMONG BASEBALL PLAYERS SEEM TO BOTHER SOME PEOPLE.. DOES THIS AFFECT YOU?

3-1

DEFINITELY!

MY TEAM CHARGES ME WAY TOO MUCH TO LET ME PLAY!

OKAY, TEAM.. WE LOST, BUT LET'S BE GOOD SPORTS ABOUT IT...

LET'S GIVE OUR OPPONENTS A GOOD OLD-FASHIONED "HIP, HIP, HURRAY!"

3-3

I HATE LOSING!

I'LL "HIP, HIP," BUT I WON'T "HURRAY!"

A D-MINUS... AAUGHH!!

A B-PLUS... AAUGHH!!

THAT PROVES IT, MA'AM..

3-6

© 1986 United Feature Syndicate, Inc.

WE ALL HAVE DIFFERENT THRESHOLDS OF PAIN!

I FEEL KIND OF ACHY TODAY

© 1986 United Feature Syndicate, Inc.

3-7

MAYBE YOUR BODY IS TRYING TO TELL YOU SOMETHING

WE'D ALL BE A LOT HEALTHIER IF WE LISTENED TO OUR BODIES..

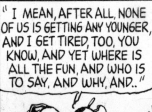

" I MEAN, AFTER ALL, NONE OF US IS GETTING ANY YOUNGER, AND I GET TIRED, TOO, YOU KNOW, AND YET WHERE IS ALL THE FUN, AND WHO IS TO SAY, AND WHY, AND.."

3-10

© 1986 United Feature Syndicate, Inc.

THIS PROGRAM WAS
BROUGHT TO YOU AS
A PUBLIC SERVICE..

CONSULT YOUR PAPER
FOR A COMPLETE LISTING
OF FUTURE PROGRAMS

AND NOW
FOR A COMMUNITY
REMINDER...

3-11

© 1986 United Feature Syndicate, Inc.

WAKE UP!

WHAT IF A GIRL GOT SO MAD BECAUSE SHE HAD TO WRITE, "I WILL NOT TALK IN CLASS" A HUNDRED TIMES THAT SHE NEVER SAID ANOTHER WORD FOR THE REST OF HER LIFE?

3-9

SO THEN WHAT IF HER PARENTS SUED HER TEACHER, THE PRINCIPAL, THE BOARD OF EDUCATION, THE STATE SUPERINTENDENT AND THE FEDERAL GOVERNMENT?

I will not talk in class.
I will not talk in class.
I will not talk in class.

WELL, I FINISHED... YOU'RE LUCKY...

WHY AM I LUCKY?

THEY WERE GOING TO SUE YOU, TOO!

3-16 © 1986 United Feature Syndicate, Inc.

WELL, WHAT DO YOU THINK?

IT WAS AN EXPERIENCE

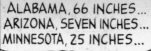

SEE, THIS TELLS YOU HOW MUCH RAIN EACH PLACE GETS IN A YEAR..

ALABAMA, 66 INCHES... ARIZONA, SEVEN INCHES... MINNESOTA, 25 INCHES...

MOUNT WAIALEALE, ON HAWAII, IS THE RAINIEST.. IT GETS 460 INCHES OF RAIN A YEAR...

WHOSE IDEA WAS THAT?

3-17

IS THAT ALL YOU'RE HAVING FOR LUNCH, SIR? JUST FRENCH FRIES?

I HAVE A THEORY THAT EATING TOO MANY FRENCH FRIES CAUSES MEMORY LOSS AND PERSONALITY ALTERATIONS...

I DOUBT IT, MARCIE..

3-18

IF THEY DID, THERE'D BE A WARNING ON THE SIDE OF EACH ONE..

YOU'RE WEIRD, SIR..

GRAMPA SAYS THIS IS THE TIME OF YEAR WHEN KIDS USED TO SHOOT MARBLES

HE SAYS YOU JUST DON'T SEE KIDS DOING THAT ANYMORE

© 1986 United Feature Syndicate, Inc.

OF COURSE NOT..

3/19

WHY WOULD ANYONE WANT TO SHOOT A MARBLE?

THIS IS HOW YOU SHOOT A MARBLE..

YOU PUT IT BETWEEN YOUR SECOND FINGER AND YOUR THUMB WITH THE TIP OF YOUR FOREFINGER UNDERNEATH..

3-20

I CAN THINK OF AN EASIER WAY...

© 1986 United Feature Syndicate, Inc.

KICK IT !!!

SCHULZ

OKAY, TEAM, IT'S TIME FOR OUR TRICK PLAY!

WHAT TRICK PLAY?

I PITCH THE BALL, THE BATTER HITS IT IN THE AIR AND YOU CATCH IT...

© 1986 United Feature Syndicate, Inc.

THAT WOULD BE QUITE A TRICK ALL RIGHT!

3-21

OH, YEAH?

3-22

TAKE THAT!

© 1986 United Feature Syndicate, Inc.

WOODSTOCK HATES IT WHEN I PUNCH HOLES IN HIS ARGUMENT...

MOLLY VOLLEY IS ON THE PHONE

SHE WANTS YOU TO BE HER PARTNER IN THE SPRING MIXED DOUBLES TENNIS TOURNAMENT

3-24

SHE'S THE ONE WITH THE FAT FACE, THE FAT BODY AND THE FAT LEGS...

SHE WANTS TO KNOW IF YOU REMEMBER HER..

VAGUELY..

SCHULZ

OKAY, PARTNER, HERE'S THE WAY IT'S GOING TO BE...

IF WE WIN, I TAKE THE CREDIT...

3-25

IF WE LOSE, YOU TAKE THE BLAME!

WHO GETS THE CHOCOLATE CHIP COOKIES?

SO HERE I AM AGAIN RIDING ON THE BACK OF MOM'S BICYCLE..

3-31

I THINK I'LL SUGGEST THAT I DO THE STEERING TODAY AND LET MOM RIDE ON THE BACK...

NO, MAYBE NOT..

© 1986 United Feature Syndicate, Inc.

MANAGEMENT ISN'T MUCH FOR TAKING SUGGESTIONS

YOU'RE ALWAYS CRITICIZING MY LUNCHES...

WELL, TAKE A LOOK AT WHAT I HAVE TODAY.. TWO SANDWICHES COTTAGE CHEESE AND AN APPLE...

4-1

NO NAPKIN RINGS!

© 1986 United Feature Syndicate, Inc.

HA HA HA HA HA HA!

YOU'RE WEIRD, MARCIE

I ALWAYS FEEL SO GUILTY..

BUT WHY SHOULD I? WHY CAN'T I JUST TAKE OFF WITHOUT SAYING ANYTHING?

4-4

NO, I ALWAYS FEEL GUILTY, AND I ALWAYS ASK...

© 1986 United Feature Syndicate, Inc.

I'M GOING INTO TOWN.. DO YOU WANT ME TO BRING YOU ANYTHING?

4-5

© 1986 United Feature Syndicate, Inc.

NOW WHAT?

HEY, MANAGER, REMEMBER OUR LAST GAME WHEN YOU WALKED SO MANY BATTERS I ALMOST FELL ASLEEP OUT IN RIGHT FIELD?

WELL, DON'T WORRY ABOUT IT...TODAY I'M READY!

PEANUTS featuring "Good ol' CharlieBrown" by SCHULZ

Game today

HI, CHUCK! YOU'VE BEEN OVER HERE, AND WATCHED SOME OF OUR GAMES, HAVEN'T YOU?

4-6

SURE, I'M ONE OF YOUR BIGGEST FANS.. YOU HAVE A GREAT TEAM..

WELL, GOOD! YOU SHOULD COME OVER TODAY BECAUSE IT'S "FAN APPRECIATION DAY"

PARTLY CLOUDY AND COOLER..

4-9

AFTERNOON SUNNY.. CLEARING TONIGHT

© 1986 United Feature Syndicate, Inc.

AND NOW, A COMMUNITY REMINDER..

DON'T REMIND ME!

Schulz

IF YOU SINK THIS PUTT, YOU'LL WIN THE TOURNAMENT..

4-10

YOU CAN DO IT..

© 1986 United Feature Syndicate, Inc.

I'M NOT SO SURE..

IT'S HARD TO PUTT WHEN YOU'RE BLEEDING INTERNALLY!

Schulz

I WAS WATCHING THIS MOVIE, SEE, WHERE THESE GUYS ARE CHASING SOME OTHER GUYS IN A CAR..

4-11

AS THEY TEAR AROUND A CORNER, THEY KNOCK OVER A FRUIT STAND, AND ORANGES FLY ALL OVER!

THEN, BOTH CARS GO ROARING OFF DOWN THE ROAD!

© 1986 United Feature Syndicate, Inc.

NO ONE EVER GOES BACK TO HELP PICK UP THE ORANGES..

Schulz

4-12

© 1986 United Feature Syndicate, Inc.

Schulz

HERE'S THE WORLD FAMOUS SERGEANT OF THE FOREIGN LEGION LEADING HIS TROOPS TO RETAKE FORT ZINDERNEUF

4-14

QUICKLY THEY MOVE THE CANNON INTO POSITION...

SLOWLY THEY MOVE THE CANNON INTO POSITION...

© 1986 United Feature Syndicate, Inc.

THEY DECIDE IT LOOKS PRETTY GOOD RIGHT WHERE IT IS...

READY, MEN? THIS IS IT!

BOOM!

GOOD GRIEF!

4-15 © 1986 United Feature Syndicate, Inc.

WHAT HAVE WE DONE TO FORT ZINDERNEUF?!

THAT CANNON BALL BLEW THE WHOLE TOP OFF YOUR DOGHOUSE!

BUT THEN WHERE DID IT GO?

I WONDER IF IT HIT ANYTHING ELSE?

4-18

THE DOCTOR IS IN

© 1986 United Feature Syndicate, Inc.

THAT CANNON BALL DESTROYED YOUR ROOF

THEN IT WENT THROUGH THE TOP OF LUCY'S PSYCHIATRIC BOOTH...

THE DOCTOR IS OUT

I WONDER WHERE IT FINALLY LANDED...

4-19 © 1986 United Feature Syndicate, Inc.

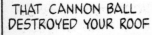  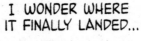

SEND YOU MONEY? I DON'T HAVE ANY MONEY! I'M JUST A LITTLE KID! WHERE WOULD I GET MONEY?!

TELL YOU WHAT I'LL DO... AFTER I FINISH COLLEGE AND GET A JOB, I'LL TRY TO SEND YOU A LITTLE, OKAY?

4-21 © 1986 United Feature Syndicate, Inc.

STOP ASKING ME!!!

I'M THE BIG SISTER AND YOU'RE THE LITTLE BROTHER! THAT'S THE WAY IT'S ALWAYS GOING TO BE!

IT'S GOING TO BE THAT WAY TODAY, TOMORROW, NEXT WEEK AND FOREVER!

4-22

☆SIGH☆

© 1986 United Feature Syndicate, Inc.

HA! I KNEW THAT'D GET A RISE OUT OF YOU!

PEANUTS

featuring

"Good ol' CharlieBrown"

by SCHULZ

4-20

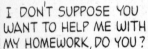

4-27

HEY LUCY.. I HEAR YOU'VE BEEN ELECTED "QUEEN OF THE MAY"

4-28

THAT'S RIGHT

© 1986 United Feature Syndicate, Inc.

CONGRATULATIONS!

THANK YOU

HERE, MARCIE..READ IT, AND SEE IF I'M NOT RIGHT...

© 1986 United Feature Syndicate, Inc.

"MAY QUEEN..."

4-29

"A GIRL CHOSEN TO BE QUEEN OF THE MERRYMAKERS ON MAY DAY AND CROWNED WITH FLOWERS"

I VOLUNTEER!

YES, MA'AM, I VOLUNTEER TO BE "QUEEN OF THE MAY"

I CAN'T VOLUNTEER?

4-30

SHE'S RIGHT, SIR..YOU HAVE TO BE CHOSEN...

OKAY, I CHOOSE ME!!

HEY, CHUCK, GUESS WHAT...I'M RUNNING FOR "QUEEN OF THE MAY" AT OUR SCHOOL!

5-1

THAT'S INTERESTING... LUCY HAS ALREADY BEEN CHOSEN AT OUR SCHOOL

YOUR SCHOOL HAS PRETTY LOW STANDARDS, HUH, CHUCK?

© 1986 United Feature Syndicate, Inc.

SHE SAYS, "CONGRATULATIONS"

GREAT NEWS, SIR! YOU'VE BEEN SELECTED TO BE OUR "QUEEN OF THE MAY"!

I KNEW IT! I KNEW I'D BE CHOSEN! JUST WAIT 'TIL THEY SEE ME LEAD THE DANCE AROUND THE MAYPOLE..

5-2

THEY CANCELED THE MAYPOLE DANCE, SIR...

OUR SCHOOL LOST ITS LIABILITY INSURANCE!

© 1986 United Feature Syndicate, Inc.

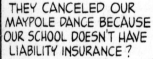   

THEY CANCELED OUR MAYPOLE DANCE BECAUSE OUR SCHOOL DOESN'T HAVE LIABILITY INSURANCE?

THAT'S RIDICULOUS!

© 1986 United Feature Syndicate, Inc.

WHO WOULD BE CLUMSY ENOUGH TO GET TANGLED AROUND A MAYPOLE?

5-3

BONK!

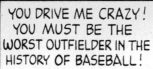

YOU DRIVE ME CRAZY! YOU MUST BE THE WORST OUTFIELDER IN THE HISTORY OF BASEBALL!

5-6

© 1986 United Feature Syndicate, Inc.

THAT'S NOT VERY ENCOURAGING!!!

I THINK YOU EXPECT TOO MUCH OF YOUR PLAYERS, CHARLIE BROWN..

5-7

AFTER ALL, WE'RE NOT PROFESSIONALS! WE'RE ONLY....

ONLY WHAT?

© 1986 United Feature Syndicate, Inc.

WHAT'S BELOW AMATEUR?

PEANUTS
featuring
"Good ol' CharlieBrown"
by SCHULZ

   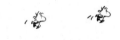

IF YOU'LL HELP ME WITH MY HOMEWORK, I PROMISE YOU UNTOLD WEALTH...

HOW MUCH IS THAT?

IF I TOLD YOU, IT WOULDN'T BE UNTOLD

5-9

© 1986 United Feature Syndicate, Inc.

I'M AMAZED AT HOW YOU FALL FOR THESE THINGS..

HOW COME WE DON'T HAVE UNIFORMS?

IF WE HAD UNIFORMS WITH NAMES AND NUMBERS, EVERYONE WOULD KNOW WHO WE ARE...

5-10

BONK!

© 1986 United Feature Syndicate, Inc.

I VOTE WE STAY ANONYMOUS

DOES EVERYONE HAVE HIS CANTEEN FILLED?

YOU CAN'T GO ON A LONG HIKE LIKE THIS WITHOUT WATER

© 1986 United Feature Syndicate, Inc. 5-12

ALWAYS REMEMBER... WATER IS OUR FRIEND..

THANKS, FRIEND

A GOOD OUTDOORS PERSON LEARNS TO PREDICT THE WEATHER

CAN ANYONE TELL ME WHAT THE WEATHER IS GOING TO BE TODAY?

"FAIR AND WARMER".. AMAZING! TELL US HOW YOU KNEW THAT...

© 1986 United Feature Syndicate, Inc. 5-13

DAILY WORLD

Dear Sweetheart,

THAT'S TOO IMPERSONAL

I THINK YOU SHOULD CALL HER SOMETHING MORE ENDEARING...

5-21

Dear Angel Food Cake With Seven Minute Frosting,

SUMMER MUST BE NEAR..

THE EVENINGS ARE WARM...

BIRDS ARE SITTING IN FRONT OF THEIR NESTS..

5-22

..IN THEIR LITTLE ROCKING CHAIRS..

GOOD AFTERNOON, MANAGER.. I'M THE PHOTOGRAPHER FOR OUR SCHOOL PAPER...

PUT THESE ON, WILL YOU, PLEASE?

© 1986 United Feature Syndicate, Inc.

TRUNKS ?!

5-26

FOR OUR SWIMSUIT ISSUE!

YOU WANT ME TO WEAR THESE?

IT'S FOR OUR SCHOOL PAPER'S SWIMSUIT ISSUE..

PUT 'EM ON..I'LL BET YOU'LL LOOK GREAT...

© 1986 United Feature Syndicate, Inc.

5-27

SEE? VERY MACHO!

SCHULZ

WELL, HERE IT IS.. OUR SCHOOL PAPER'S LONG AWAITED SWIMSUIT ISSUE!

THERE I AM ON THE COVER! WOW! WAS IT A SELLOUT?

NOT QUITE

5-30

BUT YOU SOLD MORE THAN YOU'VE EVER SOLD BEFORE, DIDN'T YOU?

NOT QUITE

© 1986 United Feature Syndicate, Inc.

SCHULZ

HOW MANY DID YOU SELL?

NONE!

CARE FOR A COOKIE?

© 1986 United Feature Syndicate, Inc.

IT'S COCONUT, ISN'T IT? IT'S COCONUT!!

5-31

TAKE IT AWAY! TAKE IT AWAY!

SCHULZ

I CAN TELL RIGHT AWAY IF I'M IN THE SAME ROOM WITH A COCONUT COOKIE...

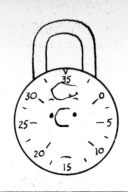

PEANUTS
featuring
"Good ol' Charlie Brown"
by Schulz

WHAT'S THIS?

THESE ARE OUR NEW SAFETY DESKS, CHARLIE BROWN

SAFETY DESKS?

WHAT DO THEY CALL THOSE THINGS THAT FALL OFF OF TREES?

YOU MEAN LEAVES? PINE CONES?

NO.. NO...

© 1986 United Feature Syndicate, Inc.

YOU DON'T MEAN BIRDS, DO YOU?

THAT'S IT! BIRDS!!

YOU REALLY ARE WEIRD, SIR..

Schulz

6/4

EXCUSE ME..

I HAVE A QUESTION FOR YOU

© 1986 United Feature Syndicate, Inc.

IF THERE ARE ALREADY 700,000 ATTORNEYS IN THIS COUNTRY, WHY DO WE NEED YOU?

ATTORNEYS HATE QUESTIONS LIKE THAT!

Schulz

6-5

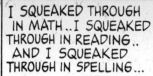

ARE'NT YOU THE GIRL I SAW ON THE PLAYGROUND YESTERDAY? WHAT ARE YOU DOING HERE?

I'M NOT SUPPOSED TO CROSS THE STREET ALONE

NO PROBLEM.. I'LL GO WITH YOU... MY PLEASURE..

I TOLD YOU MY NAME IS LINUS, DIDN'T I? IT'S A PLEASURE JUST TO BE WALKING WITH YOU...

THANKS, MISTER

MISTER?

I WALKED ACROSS THE STREET WITH HER... THAT'S ALL I DID!

YOU KNOW WHAT SHE SAID? SHE SAID, "THANKS, MISTER"

I'M ONLY TWO MONTHS OLDER THAN SHE IS, AND SHE CALLS ME "MISTER"!!

I WALKED ACROSS THE STREET WITH A GIRL ONCE, AND SHE SAID, "SO LONG, NOODLENECK!"

© 1986 United Feature Syndicate, Inc.

6-11

6-12

WELL, HI! FANCY MEETING YOU HERE.. REMEMBER ME? LINUS VAN PELT?

I'LL HAVE MINT CHOCOLATE CHIP, PLEASE

I'LL HAVE THE SAME, PLEASE...

YOU LIKE MINT CHOCOLATE CHIP? I'M SURPRISED...

6-13

MOST OLDER PEOPLE LIKE VANILLA!

© 1986 United Feature Syndicate, Inc.

SO I ORDERED MINT CHOCOLATE CHIP JUST LIKE SHE DID, AND SHE SAID SHE WAS SURPRISED...

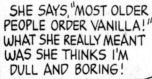

SHE SAYS,"MOST OLDER PEOPLE ORDER VANILLA!" WHAT SHE REALLY MEANT WAS SHE THINKS I'M DULL AND BORING!

6-14   © 1986 United Feature Syndicate, Inc.

I'VE ALWAYS LIKED VANILLA

EXCUSE ME..MAYBE I HAVE NO RIGHT TO ASK YOU THIS, BUT...

DIDN'T I SEE YOU YESTERDAY WITH ANOTHER KID WHO MUST BE AT LEAST A YEAR OLDER THAN YOU?

I'M ONLY TWO MONTHS OLDER THAN YOU..WHY IS HIS AGE OKAY BUT MINE ISN'T?

© 1986 United Feature Syndicate, Inc.

6-16

THERE'S OLDER, AND THEN THERE'S OLDER!

MAY I SPEAK TO YOU ABOUT MY FRIEND HERE?

I THINK YOU'RE WRONG ABOUT HIS BEING TOO OLD FOR YOU..

6-17

IN MANY WAYS, HE'S STILL QUITE YOUNG..

© 1986 United Feature Syndicate, Inc.

I MEAN, YOU SHOULD SEE HIM WITH HIS BLANKET..

AAUGH!

 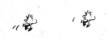 

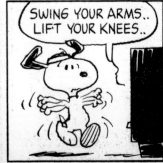

FEAR CAN TAKE CONTROL OF OUR VERY LIVES!

FEAR OF POVERTY.. FEAR OF ILLNESS...

IF YOU WERE TO ASK ME WHAT MY GREATEST FEAR IS, DO YOU KNOW WHAT I'D SAY?

CANCELLATION!

6-20

© 1986 United Feature Syndicate, Inc.

LONG HAIR IS OUT, YOU KNOW

SHORT HAIR IS IN..

© 1986 United Feature Syndicate, Inc.   6-21

ON THE OTHER HAND, MAYBE I WAS WRONG

PEANUTS
featuring
"Good ol' Charlie Brown"
by SCHULZ

June 15

Last week I was invited to sing in our local choir.

And it's always exciting to work with my rock collection.

OWOOO!

Anyway, Dad, have a happy Father's Day. your son, Spike

6-15

P.S. If you really want to, you can worry about me.

SCHULZ

6-23

I WONDER IF I SNORED LAST NIGHT..

I DID?

HEY, MANAGER, IT'S TOO HOT OUT HERE!

YESTERDAY YOU SAID IT WAS TOO COLD! MAKE UP YOUR MIND!

6-24   © 1986 United Feature Syndicate, Inc.

IT'S TOO NICE OUT HERE!

IN CASE YOU'RE INTERESTED, THERE'S A ZAMBONI HEADED YOUR WAY!

WHAT'S A ZAMBONI?

© 1986 United Feature Syndicate, Inc.

A ZAMBONI IS THE MACHINE THAT RESURFACES THE ICE BETWEEN PERIODS AT A HOCKEY GAME...

6-27

I'M TOO YOUNG TO BE RESURFACED!

?

BEEP BEEP

© 1986 United Feature Syndicate, Inc.   6-28

WHY CAN'T I HAVE A NORMAL GROUNDSKEEPER LIKE EVERYONE ELSE?

WELCOME TO THE FIRST MEETING OF OUR POLKA CLUB!

WE'RE ALL HERE TO HAVE A GOOD TIME SO LET'S GET STARTED..

CHOOSE YOUR PARTNERS!

DO YOU COME HERE OFTEN?

HELLO?

NO, I CAN'T... NOT TOMORROW..

YEAH, THE DENTIST..

I HAVE TO GO HAVE MY TEETH CRITICIZED!

Other *Snoopy* books published by Ravette

Colour landscapes

First Serve	£2.95
Be Prepared	£2.95
Stay Cool	£2.95
Shall We Dance?	£2.95
Come Fly With Me	£2.95
Let's Go	£2.95
Are Magic	£2.95
Hit The Headlines	£2.95

Black and white landscapes

It's a Dog's Life	£2.50
Roundup	£2.50
Freewheelin'	£2.50
Joe Cool	£2.50
Chariots For Hire	£2.50
Dogs Don't Eat Dessert	£2.50
You're on the Wrong Foot Again, Charlie Brown	£2.50

Snoopy Stars Series

No. 1	The Flying Ace	£1.95
No. 2	The Matchmaker	£1.95
No. 3	The Terror of the Ice	£1.95
No. 4	The Legal Beagle	£1.95
No. 5	The Fearless Leader	£1.95
No. 6	Man's Best Friend	£1.95
No. 7	The Sportsman	£1.95
No. 8	The Scourge of the Fairways	£1.95
No. 9	The Branch Manager	£1.95
No. 10	The World Famous Literary Ace	£1.95
No. 11	The Great Pretender	£1.95
No. 12	The Dog-Dish Gourmet	£1.95

Weekenders

No. 1	Weekender	£4.95

All these books are available at your local bookshop or news-agent, or can be ordered direct from the publisher. Just tick the titles you require and fill in the form below. Prices and availability subject to change without notice.

Ravette Books Limited, 3 Glenside Estate, Star Road, Partridge Green, Horsham, West Sussex RH13 8RA

Please send a cheque or postal order, and allow the following for postage and packing. UK: 45p for one book plus 30p for each additional book.

Name ....

Address ....

....